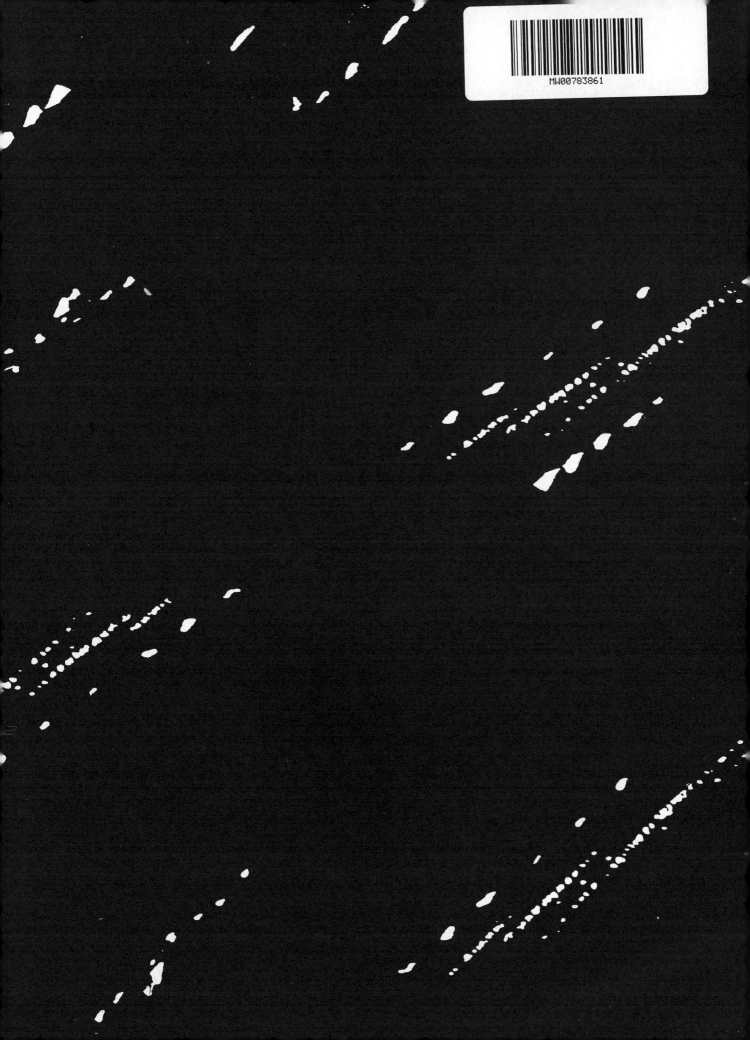

MW00783861

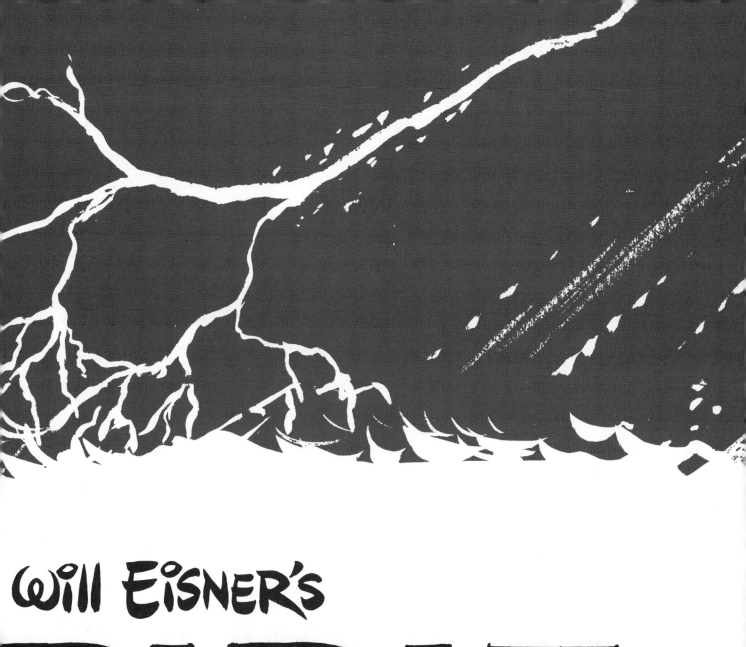

WILL EISNER'S SPIRIT

CASEBOOK

CONTENTS

THE SPIRIT CASEBOOK

writer and artist
Will Eisner

publisher
Denis Kitchen

art director
Amie Brockway

design and production
Monte Beauchamp, Diane Egbert,
Kevin Lison and Jan Manweiler

cover color
Peter Poplaski and Ray Fehrenbach

editor
Dave Schreiner

proofreader
Doreen Riley

vp, deputy publisher
Judith Hansen

vp, production
Jim Kitchen

vp, business affairs and operations
Scott Hyman

vp, chief financial officer
Dean Zirolli

sales and marketing director
Jamie Riehle

director licensing and merchandise
James Prindle

sales manager
Gail "Ziggy" Zygmont

customer service manager
Karen Lowman

managing editor
John Wills

warehouse manager
Vic Lisewski

First Printing: 1990   9 8 7 6 5 4 3 2

Who Is The Spirit?

Beneath the gnarled surface of Wildwood Cemetery, an abandoned graveyard on the outskirts of Central City, is a home. In a subterranean apartment built with the durability of an air raid shelter, and equipped with all the latest of crimefighting equipment, lives Denny Colt, alias The Spirit. He took up residence there in June of 1940.

From this sanctuary during the 12 years that followed, this great crimefighter sallied forth to do battle with the underworld. His true identity (a dark secret) was known only to Police Commissioner Dolan and his daughter, Ellen. Shielded from the restrictions that beset an ordinary legally constituted sleuth, this loner, this unorthodox fighter in the shadowy battleground of crime, became a legend in his time. In the years that passed he became enormously successful in his trade and highly regarded by the society he tried to protect. To this statement, one must add that it hasn't been easy.

How did he come to be, and who asked him, anyhow?

Well, to be candid, nobody. He plied his trade with unquestioning acceptance, and he entered the profession much the same way most people enter a lifelong career—through a combination of need, talent, and circumstance.

On the eve of World War II, our western society was suffering from severe social disruptions and economic disasters. What people wanted was help in the form of quick and easy solutions.

They got it.

In Russia they got Stalin ("Ironman"). In Germany, they got Hitler. And in America they got Superman, Batman, Plastic Man, Captain America, Captain Marvel, and a slew of others who could solve problems and deal with enemies with one blow.

It was pretty easy to become a superhero in those days because all you needed was a uniform (solid red or solid blue, and tight fitting), some kind of super power, and "SHAZAM" (or words to that effect), and you were in business. It was good business, too. Superman was reported to have grossed about ten million dollars about the time the original authors got around to petitioning the publisher for a piece of their own creation. Super-heroism was a good business because nobody questioned the credibility of the concept. Under the American free enterprise system, no one would dare stop them.

By the time Denny Colt entered the field, all the good gimmicks had been taken. Superman had come from Krypton and was masquerading as Clark Kent. Batman was a wealthy ne'er-do-well who could afford to indulge his rather questionable taste for masquerading without a license. Denny Colt had to do it the hard way. No super powers, no vast source of wealth, no uniform gave him an edge over the dark forces of evil that beset society. He had to fight crime uninsulated. He always ran the risk of getting the stuffings kicked out of him.

This, in fact, happened to him with disturbing regularity. Why he pursued this racket was always a mystery to me. As his creator, I can assure you that he had no neurotic or deep-seated psychological needs to satisfy. He was simply a guy who had a perfectly acceptable trade—that of chasing and catching crooks. He was good at it. He got into the superhero business by accident; stumbled into it, you might say.

Doctor Cobra, a psychotic who had majored in chemistry, thought he could control the world (starting with Central City) by using a chemical formula which could place entire populations in a state of suspended animation. By putting the infernal stuff into the city's water supply, he pulled the whole thing off in 24 hours.

Naturally, Denny Colt was on this guy's trail. He caught up with Cobra in the sub-cellar of an old waterfront warehouse. In the fight that followed, Granch, Cobra's bodyguard, lit into Colt and left our hero lying in the fluid—in a state of suspended animation. Well, when Commissioner Dolan appeared, it looked as if Colt was stone dead. So, with the usual ceremonies, the crimefighter was buried in Wildwood Cemetery.

And a day later, when the fluid wore off, Colt worked his way out of the grave. Now, Denny was not stupid. He could see a good deal as well as the next guy. This was a tailor-made opportunity. With no super powers, with no inherited wealth, he took the only logical course. He put a blue mask on his face, got himself a pair of gloves, and went into business for himself. From now on, he would be fighting criminals of a more realistic dimension. Here, I submit, is a pure example of traditional American enterprise and individualism.

Now with the world believing him dead, armed only with the cloak of anonymity and his hard fists, The Spirit strode forth to fight crime and criminals beyond the reach of the law. There was, however, one major characteristic with which he had to deal. The Spirit was for real; he was human, made of flesh and blood and therefore killable.

If I, his author, had any illusions about what The Spirit could and would do, it was quickly straightened out by the character himself. Actually, all an author can do is place his hero in a situation and watch him work his way out.

The stories in this book are selected from those that appeared after World War II. By the time I left the Army and returned to civilian life, returned to the task of recounting The Spirit's life, he had settled into dealing with the more mundane realities of city life. By this time, also, some of his more attractive adversaries had become familiar players in these tales. The themes had begun to become more meaningful than the usual "chase and bash" so common to mainstream comic book adventure. The Spirit, however, stuck to the role for which he was originally designed—a middle class crimefighter. Enjoy.

Will Eisner
Florida, 1990

Two Lives

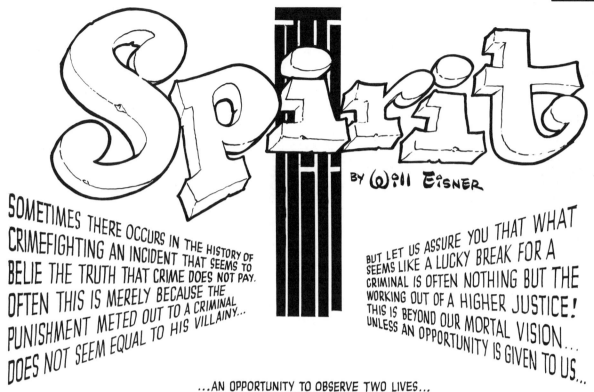

SOMETIMES THERE OCCURS IN THE HISTORY OF CRIMEFIGHTING AN INCIDENT THAT SEEMS TO BELIE THE TRUTH THAT CRIME DOES NOT PAY. OFTEN THIS IS MERELY BECAUSE THE PUNISHMENT METED OUT TO A CRIMINAL DOES NOT SEEM EQUAL TO HIS VILLAINY...

BUT LET US ASSURE YOU THAT WHAT SEEMS LIKE A LUCKY BREAK FOR A CRIMINAL IS OFTEN NOTHING BUT THE WORKING OUT OF A HIGHER JUSTICE! THIS IS BEYOND OUR MORTAL VISION... UNLESS AN OPPORTUNITY IS GIVEN TO US...

...AN OPPORTUNITY TO OBSERVE TWO LIVES...
AT THE SAME TIME...

ORIGINALLY PUBLISHED DECEMBER 11, 1948

...**A**ND SO...AS WE SAID...

WHO AMONG US CAN ACCURATELY SAY WHAT IS A FIT PUNISHMENT??

OR...IN THE WORDS OF HIS IMPERIAL MAJESTY, GILBERT & SULLIVAN'S EARNEST MIKADO OF JAPAN...

♪ My object all sublime
      I shall achieve in time
    To let the punishment fit the crime
      The punishment fit the crime...♪

CARBOY T. GRETCH   PAGE 7

CRANFRANZ QWAYLE   PAGE 7

SOLITARY CONFINEMENT

It will take you ten minutes to read this story...

... a very short time in any man's lifetime.

But these ten minutes that you will spend here are an eternity for one man.

For they are the last ten minutes in Freddy's life.

ORIGINALLY PUBLISHED SEPTEMBER 11, 1949

The time is now 10:33

TICK TICK
TICK TICK
TICK TICK
TICK TICK
TICK

WOW...AIN'T THIS HEAT MURDER? I'M TELLIN' YA, HEAT LIKE THIS CAN KILL YA...CAN Y' IMAGINE HEAT LIKE THIS IN SEPTEMBER?

MAX!

OH... NICE GUN, FREDDY...WHERE'DJA PICK IT UP? I ONCE HAD A .45... PICKED IT UP IN TH' FIRST WAR... I...

EMPTY OUT THE TILL, MAX.

FREDDY!..WHAT IS THIS, A JOKE 'R SUMPIN'? CUT TH' COMEDY!

O.K. I'LL DO IT MYSELF!

NO..NO... DON'T TOUCH THAT, YOU BUMMER!!

BANG

FREDDY... YOU ARE ONE OF THE NEIGHBORHOOD BOYS...I...KNEW YOU... SINCE...YOU WAS...A...KID... UGH...

MAX... I DIDN'T MEAN IT... BELIEVE ME, MAX...

I NEEDED DOUGH TO LEAVE TOWN...I'M SICK O' THIS BLOCK...A FRESH START...THAT'S ALL I WANT...

MAX... GET UP... HA HA... STOP KIDDIN..MAX... F'HEAVEN'S SAKE GET UP!

I'M MRS. SCHMIDT...WHERE'S MY PHONE CALL... WHICH BOOTH?

SUPER ICE CREAM

ONE

HELLO..HELLO... WHO? CHARLIE? OH, HELLO CHARLIE...YEAH.. CHARLIE....

HIYA, FREDDY! WHAT'RE YOU DOIN' BEHIND THE COUNTER? WHERE'S MAX?

3

The time now is 10:35

TICK TICK TICK TICK TICK TICK TICK TICK TICK

MAX? Y'WANNA KNOW WHERE MAX IS?...HE... HE'S OUT! I'M HELPIN' 'IM!

ALWAYS HELPIN' PEOPLE, AIN'T YA, FREDDY? TWO MALTEDS!

I ALWAYS SAID FREDDY WAS SWEET!

WHAT FLAVOR?

CHOCOLATE.

TEE HEE... WHY AIN'T YOU SWEET LIKE FREDDY, MILTY?

O.K..O.K! SO FREDDY'S A GOOD BOY! SO I AIN'T! NOW, CUT IT!

I ALWAYS THOUGHT YOU WERE SWEET, FREDDY! C'MERE...Y'GOT SOMETHIN' ON YOUR CHEEK!

LOOKS LIKE BLOOD... LET ME WIPE IT OFF...

The time
is now
10:37

TICK TICK
TICK
TICK TICK
TICK
TICK
TICK
TICK
TICK

5

The time
now is
10:39

TICK TICK
TICK TICK
TICK TICK
TICK
TICK
TICK

HOW DID IT ALL HAPPEN ??..I NEVER DID NOTHIN'... I'M TIRED...THE **COPS**... O.K... **TAKE ME!** ..I WON'T RUN ANY MORE..

HEY YOU!

SCREE

WHERE'S MAX'S CANDY STORE LOCATED AROUND HERE?

T..TWO... TWO BLOCKS DOWN...

POLICE

I TELL YA, SPIRIT... THIS NEIGHBORHOOD IS LIKE A LIT FIRECRACKER... EVERY TWO WEEKS, A MURDER...

POLICE DEPT.

HOWDYA LIKE THAT? I MUST BE CHARMED! HA HA.. **HA HA HA!!** TOO BAD, COPS... YOU HAD YOUR CHANCE.

I...I'LL GO TO FLORIDA, LIKE I PLANNED... IT'S ALL WORKIN' OUT! MAX'S DOUGH WILL LAST TILL I FIND A JOB...THEN I'LL BE HONEST AGAIN!

SORRY, PAL....WE CAN'T CASH A TWENTY!

CHANG BOOT

OH... OH, YEAH... SORRY... CHANGE... CHANGE... HERE, I...
OOPS..
@*#@ee':!!

...YOUR MONEY?

YEH..THANKS..

THE KILLER

THE SPIRIT BY Will Eisner

According to statistics, millions of Americans read millions of the most carefully written crime and crime detection stories in the world! Expertly told .... and prepared, after exhaustive research....the best of these are, in effect, lessons in crime and criminal psychology! Yet could **you**, sitting in the trolley or bus or subway at night, pick out the Killer sitting opposite you?

...TAKE THE MAN SITTING OPPOSITE US *NOW! TEST YOURSELF!*

KIND? ☐ ☐
RESPECTABLE? ☐
HONEST? ☐

YOU'RE WRONG! HE'S A MURDERER!!! MURDERER!!!

COME···COME WITH US PAST HIS PLEASANT FACE, DOWN THROUGH THE DARK CORRIDORS OF HIS BRAIN TO THE FARTHEST CORNER OF HIS MIND·····

ORIGINALLY PUBLISHED DECEMBER 8, 1946

THERE TUCKED AWAY IN A WRINKLE OF MEMORY LIES THE SEED... PLANTED IN 1942 ... FED BY SPLEEN AND SPITE... NURTURED FOR HARVEST THIS YEAR...

AND SO··· HENRY CAME HOME···

NO··· THERE'S NO OTHER POSITION OPEN, NO NEED FOR SALESMEN, WE GOT ALL THE BUSINESS WE NEED··· AND HURRY WITH THEM PACKAGES!

Y-YES, MISTER JAMES!

PACKING DEPT.

···Y'MAY HAVE BEEN A HOT SHOT SOLDIER···

···BUT YOU'RE JUST A PUNK SHIPPING CLERK TO ME··· HEY!! YOU CAN'T QUIT! I'LL BLACKBALL YOU IN THE INDUSTRY!

SUBWA

ALL ABOARD···

···LOTSA ROOM FOLKS··· UGH!

HSST! SLIP IT IN TH' JOIK'S POCKET, ATAWAY, TRIGG!

DAILY NE
GOP LANDSLIDE IN MIDDLEWEST

HENRY'S A CRACK SHOT···

HENRY'S PARTISANS LEFT NO NAZIS

···ALIVE··· PUNK! FOOL! ··· BACK IN THE SAME OLD RUT ···FOR THE REST OF YOUR LIFE··· DAY AFTER DAY···PUSHED AROUND·· HEY!! WHAT'S THIS IN MY POCKET?

AND SO THERE HE SITS...UNTIL THE TRAIN STOPS AT COURTHOUSE SQUARE...

THE SPIRIT BY Will Eisner

AH...HERE YOU ARE! BEEN MEETING EVERY TRAIN SINCE YOU PHONED!

DID YOU FIND MARY??

YEAH! SHE'S DEAD! YOU'VE GOT LOTS OF EXPLAINING TO DO, HENRY!

I KNOW!

HE AIDED THE STATE, DOLAN...IT SHOULD HELP SOME...THERE ARE "HUMAN" JURIES, Y'KNOW!

COULD BE! BUT WHAT I WANNA KNOW IS, WHY DIDJA SHOOT MARY?

I'M AFRAID YOU'LL NEVER KNOW, COMMISSIONER!

WELL, WHADDYA KNOW... HE WAS A CONVICT...AND A VETERAN'S BUTTON ON HIM, TOO!

NOW, WHY WOULD A GUY LIKE THAT GO WRONG? Y'D THINK HE'D BE SO GLAD TO BE BACK HOME HE WOULDN'T HAVE TIME T'GET MIXED UP! NOW, IF Y'ASK ME...

WELL, NO ONE'S ASKING YOU!!

NOW, WHAT DID I SAY??

THE SPIRit

BY Will Eisner

This is "Wild" Rice . . . . . may heaven help her
and this is the short story of her life.

Rice Wilder was born to wealth. Yet, even though she had all that money could buy, she felt caged... Yes, trapped in a world of gold and jewels that made an invisible cell about her...She just had to escape..

With this terrible choking fire within her, she grew up... wild, unmanageable, unable to explain the trapped feeling that throttled her. But the web of circumstance kept closing in on the strange, lonely girl.. now called "Wild" Rice.

So at intervals she would try to escape. At first she attempted to run off..but she was caught. Then she tried stealing, but her father's money covered her. Sometimes the "feeling" left her, and she appeared sweet...but soon the madness would return...like the tide.

At last...by the time she was 24 years old, the inner fires seemed to subside... and though they lay like glowing coals within her, she surrendered. Her father arranged a profitable marriage and a wedding day was set.

On the evening of the reception, however, the slumbering volcano burst within her, and the force of it sent her flying from the dance..propelled her from her husband's arms and upstairs to her room...

I CAN'T... I CAN'T GO THROUGH WITH IT... JUST ANOTHER LINK IN THE CHAIN..!

ORIGINALLY PUBLISHED APRIL 4, 1948

OH..!

A THIEF! HELP... POLICE!

YA WASTIN' Y'R TIME, LADY ...THAT MOB DOWNSTAIRS IS TOO BUSY YATTATTIN' T'HEAR YA...

SO YOU JUST SIT STILL LIKE A GOOD LITTLE GIRL WHILE I FINISH THE JOB, AN' DON'T TRY ANYTHING FUNNY!

ARE YOU REALLY A CRIMINAL...? IT MUST BE VERY EXCITING!

SOMETIMES IT IS... SOMETIMES IT AIN'T...

YOU DON'T LOOK LIKE A CRIMINAL...

GET OUTTA MY LIGHT, WILLYA?

NOW, YOU'RE GONNA GO BACK TO THE PARTY ...AND NOT TELL NOBODY WHAT YOU SEEN ... AREN'T YA?

I..I GUESS SO..

GOOD GIRL... YA KNOW, YER A REAL LOOKER ...TOO BAD YER A SOCIETY DAME...

2

MEANWHILE...

GOOD MORNING, MISS RICE... SOMETHING I CAN DO FOR YOU?

I'VE GOT A GUN, MR. JOHNSON ...HAND OVER THE MONEY...

HEH HEH MISS RICE.. ALWAYS JOKING, AREN'T YOU..?

NEXT DAY...

THEN YOU CAN POSITIVELY IDENTIFY THIS AS YOUR DAUGHTER'S SCARF..?

OH YES, YES...HAVE YOU FOUND HER? IS SHE SAFE?

NO... WE HAVEN'T FOUND HER..BUT THAT'LL BE ALL FOR NOW..

NOW WHAT WAS ALL THAT ABOUT?

DOLAN...I DIDN'T WANT TO SAY IT IN FRONT OF THE OLD MAN, BUT RICE WILDER IS WORKING WITH THE MIKE CALIBAN GANG...THIS SCARF WAS FOUND AFTER THE PEOPLE'S BANK HOLDUP...

YOU MEAN..RICE WILDER IS THE "GIRL BANDIT" THE PAPERS HAVE BEEN SCREAMING ABOUT? THEN IS SHE OR ISN'T SHE KIDNAPPED?

THAT'S WHAT I'M GOING TO FIND OUT!

CLICK

CALIBAN'S HIDEOUT..

NOT THAT I'M NOSIN' INTA Y'R PERSONAL AFFAIRS, MIKE, BUT WHY DON'T YA GET RID OF THAT DAME? SHE'S GETTIN' US TOO MUCH PUBLICITY!

I GOT MY REASONS..

...And they say down at head-quarters...Wild Rice died with a strange, pleased smile on her lips... It was a thing no one seemed able to explain...except perhaps the Spirit...and he said they wouldn't understand....

A CITY IS A LIVING THING... IT IS A BREATHING, PULSATING, MAN-MADE PHENOMENON WHOSE FOUNDATIONS GO DEEP INTO THE EARTH... THERE, IN THE WET CATACOMBS OF ITS ROOTS, TEEMS A LIFE QUITE UNKNOWN TO US IN THE FOREST OF TOWERS ABOVE..

BY WILL EISNER

ORIGINALLY PUBLISHED FEBRUARY 22, 1948

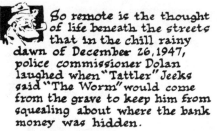

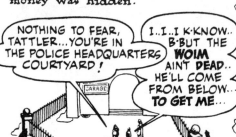

..And so...
in the silence of
the city beneath....

OOF...

HELLO..*MR. WORM*...MY GUESS WAS RIGHT...*YOU SHOT HIM FROM THE SEWER DRAIN* IN THE COURTYARD...TATTLER IS DEAD...

NOW AIN'T THAT *TOO BAD*... HA HA HA HA HA HA

YES..AND A JURY WILL AGREE, I'M SURE...

YOU'LL HAVE TO *CATCH ME* FIRST, SPIRIT...

YEOW! OUCH..

EEEEP

UGH!

THIS IS *MY WORLD* DOWN HERE...HERE IN THE PIPES AND CATACOMBS WE GOT ONLY ONE LAW... *SURVIVAL!* THE JUDGE AND JURY IS *DEATH*....YEAH, THE TABLES IS TOINED, SPIRIT...HA HA HA...

HEH HEH

WELCOME TO OUR FAIR CITY, SON...

CACKLE

47

It was now midnight of the 26th of December, 1947... a snowfall greater than the blizzard of '88 had fallen and the city lay prostrate under 25.8 inches of snow... railroads were halted... power lines down... cars and trucks lay abandoned in the streets... the once-busy metropolis lay inert and silent under a shroud of white. Atop the manhole cover stands a 2½ ton truck... immovable...

49

50

On the morning of the 27th, the city with military precision moved huge equipment into the streets and began the million-dollar job of snow removal ... life began to regain its tempo, and things long buried under the drifts began to move....

At police headquarters...

Within 48 hours the temperature dropped ...a soft rain melted the snow, saving the city millions of dollars...

....and all was normal above...

...and below the city..

The Story of GERHARD SHNOBBLE

ACTION Mystery ADVENTURE

THE SPIRIT

BY Will Eisner

BEFORE WE BEGIN THIS STORY WE WANT TO MAKE ONE POINT VERY CLEAR..

THIS IS NOT A FUNNY STORY!!

WE MEAN TO GIVE YOU A SIMPLE ACCOUNT OF GERHARD SHNOBBLE... BEGINNING AT THE POINT WHEN HE FIRST DISCOVERED HE COULD **FLY**.

PLEASE.... NO LAUGHTER....

ORIGINALLY PUBLISHED SEPTEMBER 5, 1948

GERHARD SHNOBBLE WAS BORN IN THE BIG CITY..OF ORDINARY PARENTS...AND GREW UP TO BE AN ORDINARY BOY...

EXCEPT FOR ONE LITTLE THING...

ONE DAY...

ON HIS EIGHTH BIRTHDAY, TO BE EXACT... YOUNG GERHARD SLIPPED AND FELL OFF A ROOF

IN MID-AIR HE TWISTED AND TURNED IN AN EFFORT TO SAVE HIMSELF

SUDDENLY..

HEY, MA..LOOKA ME... I'M FLYIN'!

...INSTEAD OF FALLING, HE FLEW GRACEFULLY TO EARTH.

BUT...GERHARD SHNOBBLE'S PARENTS DID NOT WANT HIM TO FLY..THEY DID NOT WANT HIM TO GO THROUGH LIFE POINTED OUT AS A STRANGE CREATURE.

NO **NO NO!** YOU MUST **NEVER** DO THAT AGAIN!

AND SO THE WHOLE THING WAS FORGOTTEN..AND GERHARD GREW UP TO BE A NORMAL, SOUND, STEADY MAN....

GERHARD SHNOBBLE.. AS A REWARD FOR YOUR FAITHFUL SERVICES THESE 35 YEARS, WE ARE PROMOTING YOU TO **NIGHT WATCHMAN** OF THE BANK.

OH THANK YOU, SIR...

BUT THAT VERY NIGHT...

W-WHO..WHO'S THERE...?

SOCK

WHAT'LL WE DO WID DE GUARD ?

OH..LOCK HIM UP IN THE VAULT..**HAW!**

C'MON.. LET'S GET OUTTA HERE !

AND THE NEXT MORNING...

GERHARD SHNOBBLE! GOOD OLD STEADY SHNOBBLE ! WHAT IS THE MEANING OF THIS ??

BUT.. BUT.. BUT SIR, I..

AFTER 35 YEARS OF TRUST IN YOU, WE FEEL BETRAYED. **SHNOBBLE..YOU ARE FIRED !**

3

WHILE GERHARD SHNOBBLE BLUNDERS SADLY THROUGH THE STREETS...

EVERY STREET AND TRAIN DEPOT IS BLOCKED.. THEY CAN'T GET OUT.

THEY **COULD** ESCAPE BY **HELICOPTER**, DOLAN..

HOLY SMOKE, SPIRIT..YOU GOT SOMETHING THERE..WE HAD A REPORT THAT A HELICOPTER LANDED ON THE ELECTRIC BUILDING LATE LAST NIGHT!

WELL..WHAT ARE WE WAITING FOR? **LET'S GET THERE AT ONCE!!**

EEEEEEEE

A FAILURE... THAT'S WHAT I AM.. A **NOBODY** WITH NO TALENT.. IF ONLY I COULD DO SOMETHING **BIG**.. THAT'D SHOW THEM!

EEOooo

DO SOMETHING.. HMF..IF ONLY.. IF ONLY I COULD.. **YES..WHY NOT?** I CAN FLY... NOW IT COMES BACK TO ME.. **I CAN FLY !!**

SCREEECH

SURROUND THE BUILDING, MEN.. THE SPIRIT IS GOING UP AFTER THEM.

HOLD THAT ELEVATOR !!

I'LL SHOW THE WORLD.. I'LL BE FAMOUS.. I'LL FLY.. **FLY!**

ROOF, PLEASE.

YES...TODAY I'LL DO IT.. TODAY THE WORLD WILL SEE...

YES, SIR.

4

AND SO... LIFELESS...
GERHARD SHNOBBLE FLUTTERED
EARTHWARD.

BUT DO NOT WEEP
FOR SHNOBBLE...

RATHER SHED A TEAR
FOR ALL MANKIND...

FOR NOT ONE PERSON IN THE
ENTIRE CROWD THAT WATCHED
HIS BODY BEING CARTED AWAY... KNEW
OR EVEN SUSPECTED THAT
ON THIS DAY GERHARD SHNOBBLE
HAD **FLOWN.**

As you know, Turkey steered a neutral course until almost the end of the war, when she broke off with the tottering Reich! At once every spy and counterspy enjoying sanctuary in Istanbul was caught floundering like a fish on the beach....yes, there I was, too, suddenly in a hostile country, and my husband none other than Hans Dammt, top Nazi in the area...

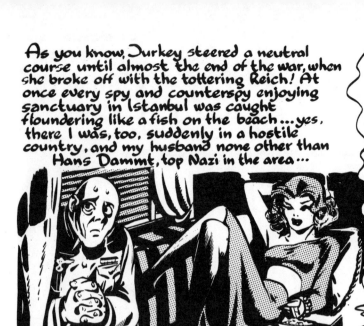

any fool could see ? he had to be done away with....

NOW DOWN DEEP INSIDE, I'M A SHY, SENSITIVE LITTLE GIRL WHO DISLIKES BLOODSHED!

...so I sought the aid of the notorious Emil Petit ---the dealer in men ---

HANS DAMMT!! MON DIEU!!.. RUSSIA, FOR ONE, WILL PAY A FORTUNE FOR HIM!

WE'LL SPLIT!

and that night...

HANS DAMMT.. EASILY WORTH A MILLION KRONER.... MY GOVERNMENT IS MOST GRATEFUL, EMIL!

YES, YES, TAKE IT AWAY, PICAR! YOU KNOW THE SIGHT OF A CORPSE DISTRESSES P'GELL!

500 THOUSAND FOR YOU...AND THE SAME FOR ME ...AHHH.... WE'RE RICH!!

TOGETHER WE'D BE RICHER! SUCH A SHAME TO SPLIT THE MILLION ...WHY DON'T WE ...AHH.... KEEP IT IN THE FAMILY?

Thus we were married....and on our honeymoon , softened by the moon and...ahem.. romance, Emil shared with me his great secret ----

P'GELL.. I AM THE SOLE POSSESSOR OF THE KALKOV FORMULA! YOU WILL KEEP IT A SECRET!!

Five days later The SPIRIT stepped into my room---

YOU SURE WASTED NO TIME, P'GELL.....YOU CONTACTED ME TWENTY-FOUR HOURS AFTER YOU LEARNED THE SECRET! HOW'D YOU EVER GET EMIL TO TELL YOU?

OH, YAAAWWN..... EASY.. MEN ARE SUCH SENTIMENTALISTS AT TIMES! HOW MUCH IS IT WORTH TO YOU?

THE KALKOV FORMULA OF PROLONGED LIFE BELONGS TO THE WORLD...TO HUMANITY!! NEITHER YOU NOR ANYONE ELSE, HAS THE RIGHT TO TRADE ON IT! I WILL TAKE IT TO AMERICA, WHERE IT WILL BE PUBLISHED FOR THE USE OF ALL!

YOU FOOL! YOU IDEALISTIC FOOL!!

I DIDN'T SEND FOR YOU BECAUSE OF THE MONEY INVOLVED... I WANT TO GO TO AMERICA... TO GET OUT OF EUROPE! I WILL TRADE THE FORMULA FOR IMMUNITY! THERE'S AN OLD SWINDLING CHARGE ON ME IN CENTRAL CITY.....

AMERICAN LAW DOES NOT PLAY THAT WAY P'GELL!

BUT THEY'LL MAKE A DEAL WITH THE SPIRIT.. AND TO MAKE IT MORE ATTRACTIVE TO YOU, I'LL ADD TO THE BARGAIN, ME... P'GELL!!

HARDLY AN ADDITION, M'LOVE!

EMIL!! ...BUT YOU WERE OUT OF TOWN...

NO! WORKING IN MY SECRET LABORATORY! BEHOLD, SPIRIT... THE LIFE, SUSTAINING LIQUID DEVELOPED BY SERGE KALKOV IN 1600!..... I WAS HIS APPRENTICE THEN ... I KILLED HIM AND KEPT IT FOR MYSELF ...UNFORTUNATELY, THE NEWS OF HIS DISCOVERY LEAKED OUT ....BUT ONLY I HAD THE LIQUID! NOW IT IS ALL GONE AND I AM 300 YEARS OLD! PERHAPS BEFORE I DIE I CAN ATONE FOR MY SIN BY GOING BACK WITH YOU, SPIRIT, AND GIVE IT TO AMERICAN SCIENTISTS!

FINE...AND I'LL SEE THAT YOU GET BACK SAFELY, EMIL!

...So, leaving me behind, Emil and the Spirit headed for the railroad....and America...

...and so...

66

And, so, as I stood there on the brink of death, The SPIRIT crossed the border and, aided by Greek friends, secured a plane-- headed for America...

A month later, Professor Cardiac of Central City's medical research center, was to announce...in a closed session--

...AND THANKS TO THE EFFORTS OF THE SPIRIT, THE ENTIRE COURSE OF OUR RESEARCH IN THE LENGTH OF LIFE MUST BE ALTERED! WITH LUCK, AND AIDED BY THIS FORMULA, WE SHOULD STARTLE THE WORLD SOON!

AND WHAT ABOUT ME?? WAS I KILLED?

OF COURSE NOT!! PICAR CHANGED HIS MIND... ER...CHARMED BY MY..AHEM... PERSONALITY... HE PROPOSED!!

...AND I COULD HARDLY REFUSE... ISTANBUL IS SO DANGEROUS FOR A POOR, DELICATE, DEFENSELESS WIDOW THESE DAYS!

And so, you can find me any afternoon in the cafés of Istanbul, with my dear husband, Picar, sipping tea and keeping an eye open for a way to turn an honest piaster. ...you see, what with a bribe here and a bad gamble there, our fortunes dwindled..temporarily--

DEATH OF AUTUMN MEWS

ACTION
Mystery
ADVENTURE

THE SPIRIT

BY Will Eisner

To the north of Central City, on a
hill overlooking the bustling metropolis,
lies abandoned Wildwood Cemetery.
Here, hidden in the tangled weedy growth,
is the hideaway of the Spirit. Accepted
by the police as a friendly 'outlaw' and
feared by the underworld, his true
identity is still a mystery.
Who is really the man behind the mask?
Every so often,
someone tries to find out...

ORIGINALLY PUBLISHED OCTOBER 9, 1949

AND SO...

LATER, APT. 14-A ROYAL TOWERS

FOUR THIEVES LED BY VIRGIL GUNBELT WERE APPREHENDED BY THE SPIRIT TONIGHT... THE THIEVES HAD BROKEN INTO THE TAPESTRY EXHIBIT AT THE CENTRAL

6★!!6★ ⓢ★ *CLICK*

THAT **DOPE** VIRGIL... I **TOLD** HIM TO LAY LOW!

...AUTUMN! I GOT IT! FROM THE SPIRIT'S OWN FILES AND THE NEWSPAPERS! I FOUND OUT WHO HE **REALLY** IS!

I GOT ALL THE PROOF! **SEE!** HE'S NO CROOK! Y'DON'T HAVE T'WORRY ANYMORE! HE'S **NOT** A OUTLAW... AND THIS PROVES IT !!

HMM... SO THE SPIRIT IS REALLY **DENNY COLT!**

HELLO, SPIRIT? THIS IS AUTUMN MEWS... I HAVE SOME INFORMATION THAT MIGHT INTEREST YOU! UNLESS VIRGIL IS RELEASED IN **ONE** HOUR... I'LL TELL ALL THE NEWSPAPERS THAT THE SPIRIT IS **DENNY COLT!**

!

THINK IT OVER, CRIME FIGHTER! I'LL BE AT THE DAILY GLOBE CITY DESK TOMORROW AT 10 A.M.!

SO! YOU WERE JUST USING ME...! **GIMME BACK THOSE PAPERS!**

SLAP

BLOW, SONNY! YOU ANNOY ME!

AND SO...

HOW COULD SHE KNOW? HOW DID SHE FIND OUT?

I DON'T KNOW.. I DON'T KNOW..

LEMME SPRING VIRGIL.. IT'LL KEEP HER QUIET UNTIL...

NO... DOLAN! YOU'RE NOT GOING TO SMEAR YOUR RECORD TO.. TO... KEEP THE SPIRIT IN BUSINESS..

6

the CHRISTMAS Spirit

BY WILL EISNER

And on this day
those who all the year
are grasping, and seek riches
from others,
pause for one brief moment
and become kind, human,
generous beings...
all that dreamers believe
men should be...

Or so the legend runs...

77

And so it came to pass
one year, not too long ago,
a heavy snow fell upon the land...
and from Central City in the south
to State Prison in the north
the little lights twinkled on
and it was Christmas.

STATE
PRISON
STOP FOR INSPECTION

SILENT NIGHT.. HOLY NIGHT... ALL IS CALM...

CHRISTMAS... *BAH!!*

R..RIP

THAT WARDEN AND HIS CHRISTMAS CAROLS... DRIVIN' ME NUTS!..ME..BASHER BAINS.. LOCKED IN A CELL...*I'M A CAGED TIGER!!*

..AND THERE'LL BE GOOD WILL TOWARD MEN...

GOOD WILL TOWARD MEN... HA HA HA HA HA

STOMP
STOMP
STOMP CRUNCH

2.

79

82

83

85

ORIGINALLY PUBLISHED SEPTEMBER 19, 1948

It was on just such a night as this that "BLACKY" MARQUETT arrived back in America from Europe... this time he had with him a war bride, one LORELEI ROX... Blacky headed immediately for the roadhouse he owned since before the war... the rest is easy to reconstruct...

LORELEI, BABY... THIS IS HOME! FROM NOW ON, NO MORE SCRABBLING IN THE RUINS OF EUROPE!

YES, SIR... WITH A LITTLE O' THE "WIFELY TOUCH" Y'CAN FIX THIS JOINT UP LIKE A PALACE... IT'S RIGHT ON THE MAIN DRAG, TOO.

HEY!! CUT OUT THAT SCREWY SINGIN' AN' LISSEN... I'M TALKIN' T'YA!

UGH.. WOTTA VOICE! ENOUGH T'DRIVE YA NUTS!

BABY

???
@*☆#&
*#@∞☆!!

...SOME PEOPLE GOT NOIVE! @☆#∞☆!! HEY... HE'S A TRUCK DRIVER...

YEAH... AND HE LEFT HIS TRUCK DOWN THE ROAD... AND IT'S LOADED WID HARD-TO-GET STUFF... HMMM.... LORELEI... WE'RE IN BUSINESS. THE HIJACKIN' BUSINESS!

BLACKY MARQUETT WAS SMART...HE ONLY PULLED JOBS LIKE THAT ABOUT ONCE EVERY TWO MONTHS. AFTER EACH HAUL HE'D WAIT WHILE THE POLICE RAN AROUND IN CIRCLES AND GOT TIRED INVESTIGATING... THEN ONE NIGHT...

TRUCK 52 COMING IN, SIR.. WE'LL UNLOAD HER AT ONCE.

ACME HAULING
INTERSTATE TRUCKING

Y'R LATE, McNABB! ...WHICH SPOILS YOUR UNUSUALLY FINE RECORD. O.K...GIT OUT...

HEY..THE LOAD'S GONE!
ASK McNABB WHAT HAPPENED.

I C.CAN'T.. HE'S DEAD!

THAT NIGHT I DROPPED IN ON BOSS WHEELER. HE WAS IN BAD SHAPE. MOST OF HIS MEN HAD QUIT, AND THE BAFFLED POLICE HAD GIVEN UP HIS CASE.

SURE, BUD... I GOT LOTSA JOBS OPEN..BUT IT'S ONLY FAIR TO WARN YA... 3 MEN BEEN KILLED SINCE SPRING. NOW Y'C'N SEE THE DISPATCHER IF Y'WANT.

I'LL TAKE A CHANCE..I.. I..ER..NEED THE DOUGH, SIR.

...SOON AS I LAID EYES ON THE DISPATCHER, I THOUGHT I HAD THE ANSWER.

SO!

WELL ..GRIFTER SNITCH.. SO YOU'RE THE TIP-OFF MAN IN THIS HIJACK, EH?
TALK..WHO'S HITTING THOSE TRUCKS?

...YES..I THOUGHT I HAD THE ANSWER...BUT I WAS WRONG. IT WASN'T GOING TO BE AS EASY AS ALL THAT.

HEY.. PUT THAT MAN DOWN ..HE WAS HIRED YESTERDAY. ..JUST CAME OUT OF JAIL ...WELL..? DO YA WANNA DRIVE OR DONTCHA?

ULP! SORRY, SNITCH, I..

... IT WAS CLEAR NOW THAT I HAD TO DO IT THE HARD WAY...LIKE GETTING MYSELF KILLED, FOR INSTANCE.

ACME HAULING CO. TRUCKING
No 17240

3

CROSS-COUNTRY DRIVING IS A TOUGH JOB..THE MONOTONY..THE UNBROKEN HUM OF THE MOTOR..ALL FORM A SORT OF HYPNOTIC INFLUENCE... ...SOON I FOUND MYSELF THINKING THAT NOTHING WAS GOING TO HAPPEN ON THIS RUN...

THEN, AS I BEGAN THE LONG CLIMB UP ROUTE 5, THE HARMONIC VIBRATION NATURAL TO MOST TRUCKS ON HEAVY PULLS BEGAN TO DULL MY HEARING...

AND SUDDENLY I BEGAN HEARING MUSIC... A STRANGE KIND OF MUSIC ...PITCHED HIGH..AND YET BLENDING WITH THE "SINGING" OF THE TIRES..

I KEPT SLOWING DOWN THE TRUCK SO THAT I MIGHT BETTER HEAR THE MUSIC...

IT GOT **LOUDER**.......AND **LOUDER**

..AND IT SEEMED TO LIFT ME OUT OF MY TRUCK SEAT..

MY INSTINCTS WERE STILL DEPENDABLE.. ...I STOPPED THE TRUCK AND BRAKED IT.. **BUT MY MIND...MY BRAIN..MY NERVES WERE VIBRATING LIKE PLUCKED VIOLIN STRINGS**

I MOVED THROUGH SPACE... OR WHAT SEEMED LIKE IT...THEN SUDDENLY..!

WHAM

..THE MUSIC WAS FADING.. MY HEAD WAS CLEARING...
I TURNED TOWARD THE BLOW AND
WHAM

THE SHARP PAIN OF THAT SECOND BLOW CUT LIKE A KNIFE THROUGH THE COBWEBS IN MY BRAIN..

..I LOOKED UP...AND THERE BEFORE ME STOOD THE ANSWER...

5

I LUNGED BLINDLY.. BUT SHE ELUDED ME WITH CAT-LIKE EASE...

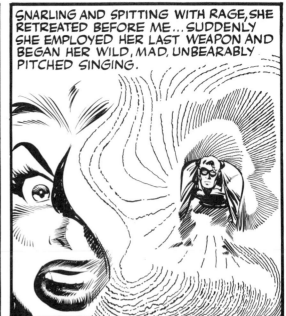

SNARLING AND SPITTING WITH RAGE, SHE RETREATED BEFORE ME... SUDDENLY SHE EMPLOYED HER LAST WEAPON AND BEGAN HER WILD, MAD, UNBEARABLY PITCHED SINGING.

LOUDER AND LOUDER

...UNTIL THE WALLS SHOOK AND THE FLOOR QUIVERED WITH THE VIBRATION...

...AND SUDDENLY.. LIKE A WATER GLASS SMASHED BY SOME HEROIC TENOR'S VOICE.. THE WARPED FRAME BUILDING COLLAPSED ABOUT US WITH A THUNDERING CRESCENDO!

...BY A MIRACLE OF GOOD LUCK I HAD CLUNG TO THE SOLID FIREPLACE... AND WE WERE ALL THAT REMAINED INTACT ABOVE THE DEBRIS THAT BURIED LORELEI... AND HER HIJACKING HUSBAND

WOW.. gulp..WHEW.. ..WHAT ABOUT WHEELER..? DOES HE KNOW THE MYSTERY IS SOLVED?

HMM.. BETTER CALL ACME TRUCKING AND JUST TELL HIM IT'S O.K. TO CONTINUE HIS SCHEDULES.

HELLO... OH YEAH..COMMISSIONER DOLAN... WHAT ??..Y'CLEARED UP THE MYSTERY ?.. NO MORE TROUBLE, EH? GOOD... THANKS ... NO, I'M GETTIN' ME TRUCKS THROUGH..YEAH, I'M HIRING LADY DRIVERS NOW !

7

91

Among those who know death best, there persists a belief that when your number is up...well, your number is up...and that is that. For in the gambling-hall of life, the game of **crime** is **fixed**... and the percentage favors...death.

BUT, YOU SAY, HOW DO YOU KNOW WHEN YOUR NUMBER'S UP?

WHY, IF A GUY KNEW **WHEN** HIS NUMBER WAS UP, HE COULD **QUIT**....AND STAY **AHEAD** OF THE GAME.

OKAY... **OKAY**...OKAY.

LET US TAKE, FOR INSTANCE...

J. Rollo Dyce, ESQ.

HE PARLAYED A TWO-CARD DRAW INTO A TEN-GRAND JACKPOT AND **KILLED HIS PARTNER** FOR THE KITTY.... NOW RIGHT THERE ROLLO **KNEW** HIS NUMBER WAS UP... BUT, SINCE HIS LUCK WAS IN, HE GATHERED UP THE ROLL AND PLAYED **"JUST ONE MORE HAND"** ....HE SCOOPED UP HIS ROLL AND PLAYED IT 100-TO-ONE...HE TOOK IT ON THE LAM.

ORIGINALLY PUBLISHED MAY 16, 1948

AND SO... WE FIND ROLLO DYCE IN CENTRAL CITY THE NEXT MORNING..

OUT OF TOWN PAPERS

CARTER CITY GANG SEEKS KILLER OF GAMBLER SHARP

HEADS IT'S THE TRIBUNE, TAILS IT'S THE JOURNAL.

TAILS... THE JOURNAL IT IS, SIR.

HMMM... LET'S SEE HOW I CAN PARLAY MY LUCK... AH!

JOURNAL

HOUSEHOLD HELP WANTED

couple..elderly. 32X Rogers Rd. after 5 p.m.

Elderly woman needs capable man to manage country estate. Mrs. Morrison..RFD 3. Bald Mountain. Box 34

Couple wanted sleep in.. light housework..must have references Call HE 29693B

Guldeharg roty

YESSIR..THERE'S A SURE BET...IT CAN'T LOSE.

SPFT

...THAT JOB WILL KEEP ME UNDER COVER FOR A FEW DAYS, AND WHEN THE HEAT'S OFF, I'LL CROAK THE OLD GAL AND TAKE HER WAD..WHICH SHE SURELY HAS... HAW... LOOKS LIKE IT'S HER NUMBER THAT'S UP!

YOUR CITY - HELP KEEP IT CLEAN

THAT EVENING...

I HOPE YOU'LL BE COMFORTABLE, MR. DYCE...IT CERTAINLY IS NICE FOR AN OLD LADY LIKE ME TO HAVE SOMEONE TO TAKE OVER THE RESPONSIBILITY OF THIS PLACE.

DON'T WORRY ABOUT A THING, MA'AM.

BY THE WAY.. YOU'LL HAVE TO SHIFT FOR YOURSELF ...THE SERVANTS DON'T ARRIVE TILL MONDAY.

REALLY...? ER...HOW CONVENIENT... AHEM..I MEAN TCH TCH! I'LL MANAGE SOMEHOW.

I'LL LOCK THE DOORS...CAN'T TAKE A CHANCE ON ROBBERS OR MURDERERS WAY OUT HERE.

HA HA HA... Y'R PRECAUTIONS ARE A WASTE O'TIME... Y'R NUMBER'S UP! CHUCKLE CHUCKLE AND Y'DON'T KNOW IT...

2

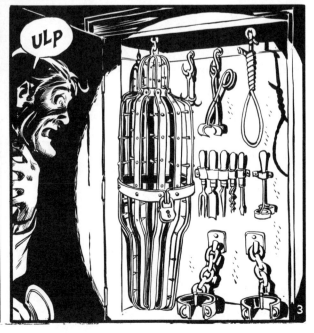

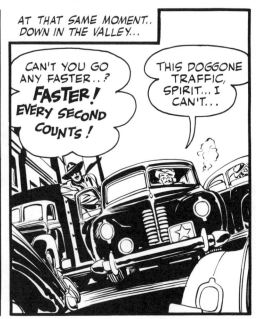

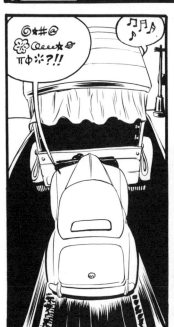

6

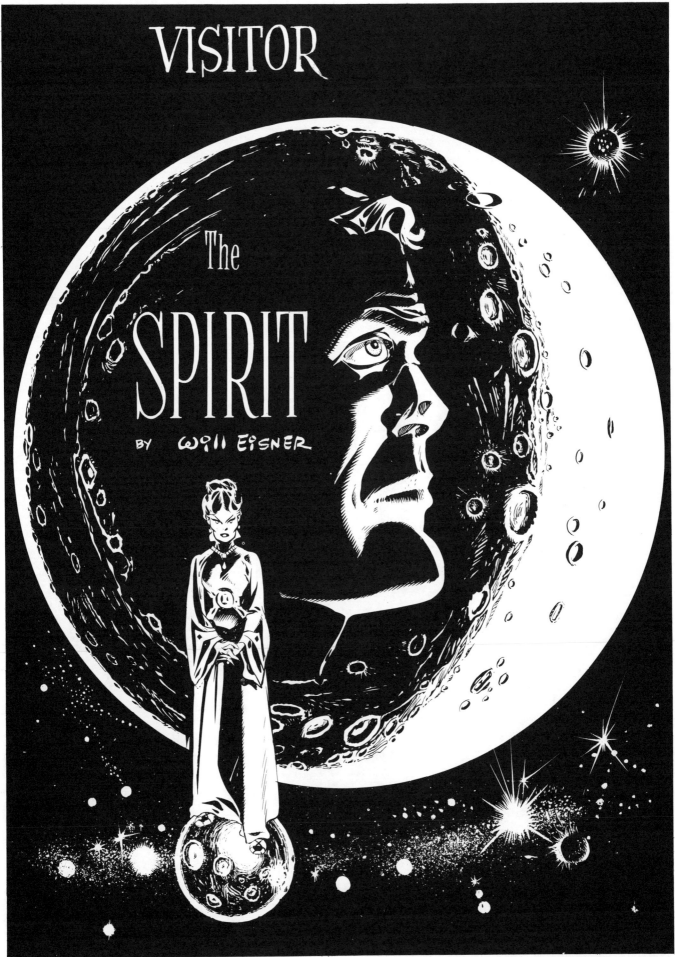

ORIGINALLY PUBLISHED FEBRUARY 13, 1949

SOMETIME BETWEEN THE HOURS OF 2:40 AND 2:53 ON THE AFTERNOON OF FEBRUARY 12, TWO GUNMEN, CRACKER BARL AND 'COMBO' NATHAN, WALKED INTO THE CENTRAL BANK WITH THE INTENTION OF COMMITTING ARMED ROBBERY.

THEY WENT TO TELLER NO. 3 AND DREW PISTOLS. THEY WOULD HAVE SUCCEEDED IN THEIR PLAN HAD NOT AN EXPLOSION OCCURRED AT THE SPOT UPON WHICH THEY STOOD.

THE FORCE OF IT KILLED BARL AND LITERALLY DISINTEGRATED THE POOR TELLER AND THE OTHER THIEF, 'COMBO' NATHAN.

.OR SO IT SEEMED...

The facts herewith (and chronologically) presented are available to us because The Spirit, long on the trail of these two, arrived on the scene within the hour...

.. STRANGE THAT THE OTHER TWO SHOULD BE SO COMPLETELY DISINTEGRATED, BUT CRACKER STILL INTACT... AND NOTICE THE ABSENCE OF BLOODSTAINS...

AND THE WALLS ARE STILL HOT... FUNNY KIND OF EXPLOSION...

WHAT IS THIS, GUARD?

IT'S A PHOTO OF MISS COSMEK... SHE GULP WAS THE TELLER.. POOR LASS BEEN HERE ONLY A YEAR.

GET ME HER HOME ADDRESS.

N-O-T BAD.. NOT B-A-D!

102

It was dusk when The Spirit at last found the beautiful Miss Cosmek's apartment..

EMPTY... NOT A STICK OF FURNITURE IN HERE! DID SHE PLAN TO LEAVE TOWN?

NO SORR... SHE'SA KEEP D'APART-E-MENT JOOSA LIKE DIS...SHE'SA TOL' ME AV'RY TEENG EESA BE KEPT EENA KONTRY HOUSE... "LOOKOUT POINT" BEACH.

WHO LIVES NEXT DOOR?

MEESTER NIMBUS.. HE'SA WORK EENA WEATHER DEPARTMENT!

NO USE YOU LOOK IN HERE EITHER...HE'SA NO GOT NOTHIN' INSIDE TOO!!

MAY I USE YOUR TELEPHONE, MRS. PIZZA??

HELLO, DOLAN... GET ME A DEPARTMENTAL CHECK ON MR. NIMBUS... HE WORKS IN THE WEATHER BUREAU... AND CALL ME BACK...

HEY.. YOU WANT SOME-A-T'EENG TO EAT WHILE-A YOU WAIT?

NO THANKS, MRS. PIZZA.

HELLO, SPIRIT.. NIMBUS IS CLEAN... NO CONNECTIONS WITH ANY SUBVERSIVE GROUPS...NO ARRESTS OF ANY KIND..WORKING AT THE BUREAU A' YEAR... A EUROPEAN METEOROLOGIST... PERSONAL HABITS STEADY... WHAT'S HE GOT TO DO WITH THIS?

OH, NOTHING, I GUESS.. BUT BEFORE I CALL IT A DAY, I'M GOING TO VISIT LOOKOUT POINT BEACH FOR A LAST CHECKUP

RING

AND SO...

THAT'S MISS COSMEK'S HOUSE, SIR.

THANKS... I'LL WALK THE REST OF THE WAY...

DZZZZT

THAT WAS FOOLISH... TRY IT AGAIN AND YOU'RE THROUGH.

⊕OM3 MARS... COSMIC DUST IN 5000 KILO GLOBULES FORMING IN STRATOSPHERE.. ALL FLIGHTS PLEASE NOTE... AGENT COSMEK... **AGENT COSMEK**... YOU WILL REPORT TO HOME BASE AT ONCE...

SO... **HE** HAS TOLD THEM ABOUT THE BANK ROBBERY... I THOUGHT **HE** WOULD COVER FOR ME... BUT NOW THEY KNOW EVERYTHING UP THERE...

WHAT ON EARTH IS THIS?

..SO **YOU** CAUSED THE EXPLOSION AT THE BANK...

..YES... DURING THE THE CONFUSION I GOT OUT... COMBO FOLLOWED ME, UNHURT.

WHAT ON EARTH? THAT'S JUST IT... IT'S **NOT** ON EARTH...

I'M AN AGENT FROM THE PLANET MARS.

WHAT ??

LISTEN TO ME...THERE'S NOT MUCH TIME, AND YOU'LL HAVE TO TAKE MY WORD FOR IT ALL... I AM A MARTIAN AGENT OF INTELLIGENCE.. THERE IS **ONE OTHER** SUCH AGENT ON EARTH ..THE ONE I CALL "HE".. MY JOB WAS TO GET INTO THE BANKING SYSTEM AND MAKE REPORTS...YESTERDAY, WHEN THOSE TWO MEN TRIED TO ROB US, THEY SPOILED EVERYTHING...I KNEW MY IDENTITY WOULD BE **DISCOVERED** IN THE POLICE INVESTIGATION THAT WOULD SURELY FOLLOW. SO...

I GET IT.: GULP.: NOW YOU'VE BEEN ORDERED **BACK** BECAUSE YOU **BUNGLED** THE JOB...

YES...YES... BUT...

BUT ??

BUT I DON'T WANT TO GO... **I DON'T WANT TO LEAVE THE EARTH !**

YOU HAVE NO IDEA WHAT IT'S LIKE THERE... **EFFICIENCY**... SCIENTIFIC RESEARCH FROM BIRTH TO DEATH... WE ARE FLESH-AND-BLOOD **AUTOMATONS**!!

HERE ON EARTH I'VE FOUND THAT ALL THE WARM EMOTIONS.. LAUGHTER..LOVE.. YES, EVEN TEARS.. ARE **FREE** FOR **EVERYONE**... BUT UP THERE SUCH EMOTIONS ARE CRIMES! **NOW**...TO GO BACK TO THAT, AFTER I'VE KNOWN THIS WONDERFUL LIBERTY.... IT.. IT'S LIKE A **LIVING DEATH!**

LISTEN... I HAVE A PLAN...WE CAN **ESCAPE** TOGETHER, YOU AND I... HIDE ME OUT IN THE MOUNTAINS FOR A YEAR... **PLEASE**.. LISTEN...

HA HA HA COSMEK..YOU'RE A FOOL..

DID YOU REALLY THINK YOU COULD PULL OUT ON YOUR PLANET LIKE THIS?? ..IF I HAD KNOWN HOW **WEAK** AND **EARTHLIKE** YOU REALLY ARE, I'D NEVER HAVE RECOMMENDED YOU FOR THE POST! YOU'RE **STUPID**! BESIDES, **WE'D GET YOU**, NO MATTER WHERE YOU RAN ON THIS PLANET!

IS THAT THE OTHER AGENT?

YES, **YES**... **STEP BACK**, SPIRIT!!

LISTEN, AGENT 'ONE'. I'M NOT AS STUPID AS YOU THINK..

I'M NOT GOING BACK ALIVE...

NOR WILL YOU HAVE THE USE OF THIS LAB...

WE'RE TOO LATE!

DON'T STAND THERE GAWKIN', KLINK.. **CALL AN AMBULANCE!**

POLICE HOSPITAL

YOU MAY SPEAK TO HER NOW, SIR...

NOW..HRMPF... MISS COSMEK... WE KNOW YOU WERE IN CAHOOTS WITH THOSE TWO ROBBERS... BETTER TELL ME THE TRUTH...

I'M AN AGENT FROM MARS.. **I'M AN AGENT FROM MARS** I TELL YOU...

SHE'S **MAD**... COMPLETELY OUT OF HER MIND! WELL, THAT'S **ONE** WAY TO BEAT A MURDER RAP!

SUPPOSE....JUST SUPPOSE I COULD PROVE SHE'S TELLING THE **TRUTH**?

TO **PROVE** IT TO ME, YOU'D HAVE TO DIG UP **ANOTHER** "AGENT" WHOSE SANITY I COULDN'T QUESTION... HEH HEH... **HEY**... WHERE YOU GOING?

..TO DIG UP THE OTHER AGENT!

ORIGINALLY PUBLISHED OCTOBER 23, 1949

The city is quiet now...the rain has stopped...and the last echo of shooting has long since caromed off into the alleys around 52 Hunter Place... On the glistening streets behind the still-twitching victims, gather the police, like hunters in the fields..while on the top floor of 52 Hunter Place, in his lair, Reynard, the fox, waits...at bay!!

POLICE

CLICK   CLICK   CLICK

PUBLIC PHONE

DING

ZZZZT

HELLO..**HELLO**...REYNARD...LISTEN TO ME...THIS IS THE SPIRIT..YOU'RE COMPLETELY SURROUNDED... IN TEN MINUTES THE POLICE WILL OPEN FIRE, AND MORE INNOCENT BYSTANDERS MAY GET HURT!..HAVEN'T YOU KILLED ENOUGH PEOPLE ALREADY? REYNARD, YOU'VE SHOT 10 MEN TO DEATH.. **YOU CAN'T GO ON THIS WAY..LISTEN TO ME.. LISTEN!!**

REYNARD... HELLO...**HELLO!!**

RING RING **RING** RING RIN RING

LET ME SEE...WHERE WAS I... OH, YES... 9:43 P.M..."I-AM-EXPERIENCING- INTERFERENCE-IN-CARRYING- THROUGH-MY- EXPERIMENT..."

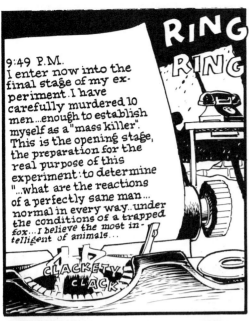

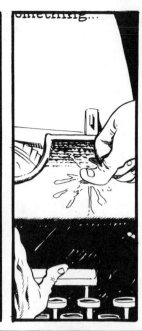

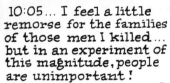

10:07... They are on the move. I don't know what their plan is.
...I shall try to draw their fire...

10:10... The fox has trapped one of the hounds!
I have the Spirit and he is helpless... shot in the legs. I will not kill him. I will let him watch my experiment...

113

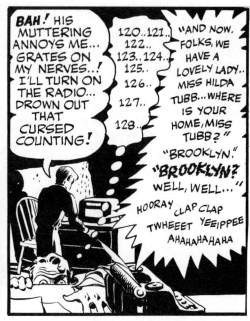

ORIGINALLY PUBLISHED NOVEMBER 27, 1949

I leave the office at five every afternoon and take the subway home.
"Home" is uptown... East Central City, 1532 Sawyer Avenue, Apartment E-10...
(that's five flights up... there is a self-service elevator...)

118

OPERATION... ALL THAT MONEY... HOW CAN I EVER AFFORD IT? ...ALL THAT MONEY...

4,000.. 5,000... 6,000..

M-MR. PARRISH..?

YOU ARE LATE, MR. STET! THE FIRM HAS LITTLE PATIENCE WITH TARDINESS!

MR. PARRISH, I'VE JUST VISITED AN EYE DOCTOR. I...

MEDICAL APPOINTMENTS CAN BE ATTENDED TO AFTER HOURS... ON YOUR OWN TIME.

.. I'M GOING BLIND!

WHAT?

..THAT IS, I WILL GO BLIND IF... IF I DON'T GET MONEY FOR AN OPERATION! ..IF I COULD BORROW $5,000 FROM THE FIRM, I...

RRISH & SON
NOTARY PUBLIC
ACCOUNTANTS

BLIND? VERY REGRETTABLE. AFTER ALL YOUR YEARS OF SERVICE. HATE TO LET YOU GO, STET!

ONLY LEND ME $5,000! I'LL BE ALL RIGHT AGAIN!

HMM...? $5,000... NO, NO! OUT OF THE QUESTION! BUT STAY TILL THE END OF THE WEEK. IT'S NOT OUR POLICY TO GIVE TWO WEEKS' PAY, BUT SINCE YOU ARE AN OLD, LOYAL, TRUSTED EMPLOYEE, WE'LL MAKE AN EXCEPTION.

I CAN'T WORK... CAN'T THINK...

TUESDAY I WENT TO THE DOCTOR...AND HERE IT IS FRIDAY.. MY LAST DAY..

OH, MY HEAD... MY HEAD!

GOING BLIND... HE TOLD ME TUESDAY, COMMISSIONER! YOU KNOW HOW WORRIED I WAS ABOUT THOSE SHORTAGES...THIS EXPLAINS IT... OBVIOUSLY ALL AN ACCOUNTING MISTAKE BY THAT POOR HALF-BLIND MAN!

THINK HE MADE THE WRONG ENTRIES, EH?

NO DOUBT ABOUT IT...ER.. AHEM... MR. STET! COMMISSIONER DOLAN WOULD LIKE A WORD WITH YOU!

THE BANKS HAVE FILED A COMPLAINT ..THERE'S A SHORTAGE OF $5,000 IN THE BOOKS. KNOW ANYTHING ABOUT IT?

$5,000...BY THE WAY... WASN'T THAT THE AMOUNT YOU NEEDED FOR YOUR OPERATION, MR. STET?

HMMM.

I'VE GOT A SPELL AGAIN!

...PARRISH IS COMING AFTER ME... GOT TO KEEP AWAY FROM HIM...THIS SPELL MAY NOT LAST.. ...GOT TO KEEP MOVING...AWAY FROM HIM...

YOU HAVEN'T A CHANCE, STET.!

I WAS IN THE FIRST WAR, MR. STET...A CAPTAIN... PRETTY GOOD SHOT, TOO...

I CAN SAY YOU CAME BACK... ADMITTED STEALING THE MONEY... THREATENED ME... EH? HOW DOES THAT SOUND?

SELF-DEFENSE.! ...I SHOT YOU TO PREVENT YOU FROM ROBBING ME.!

MY SIGHT IS COMING BACK...EVERYTHING IS BLURRED, BUT NOW I CAN SEE A BIT... RUN.!...MY ONLY CHANCE IS TO RUN... THERE'S THE DOOR...

HE'S AN OLD MAN... I CAN OUTDISTANCE HIM...

WHERE ARE YOU RUNNING, MR. STET? YOU CAN'T SEE... LOOK OUT FOR THAT LAMP...

CRASH

VERY GOOD, MR. STET.! YOU'LL MAKE IT LOOK AS IF WE STRUGGLED... ADD TO MY STORY TO THE POLICE.!

HEH HEH HEH

...HIS VOICE IS FARTHER AWAY NOW... MAYBE I'M OUT OF HIS SIGHT... I CAN BARELY SEE OUTLINES... GOT TO HIDE BEHIND SOMETHING... I MUST HIDE.!

WHERE DID YOU GO, MR. STET...? INTO ONE OF THE OFFICES? WAIT FOR ME... I'LL FIND YOU.!

IT'S A LONG NIGHT...WE HAVE QUITE SOME TIME TO PLAY OUR GAME...

HEH HEH..AS WE USED TO SAY WHEN PLAYING HIDE AND SEEK IN OUR YOUTH... "AM..I...HOT.. OR..AM..I..COLD ??"

I'VE BLACKED OUT AGAIN.!

I'M NOW COMPLETELY BLIND.!

HE'S...GOT..ME.. NOW...

6

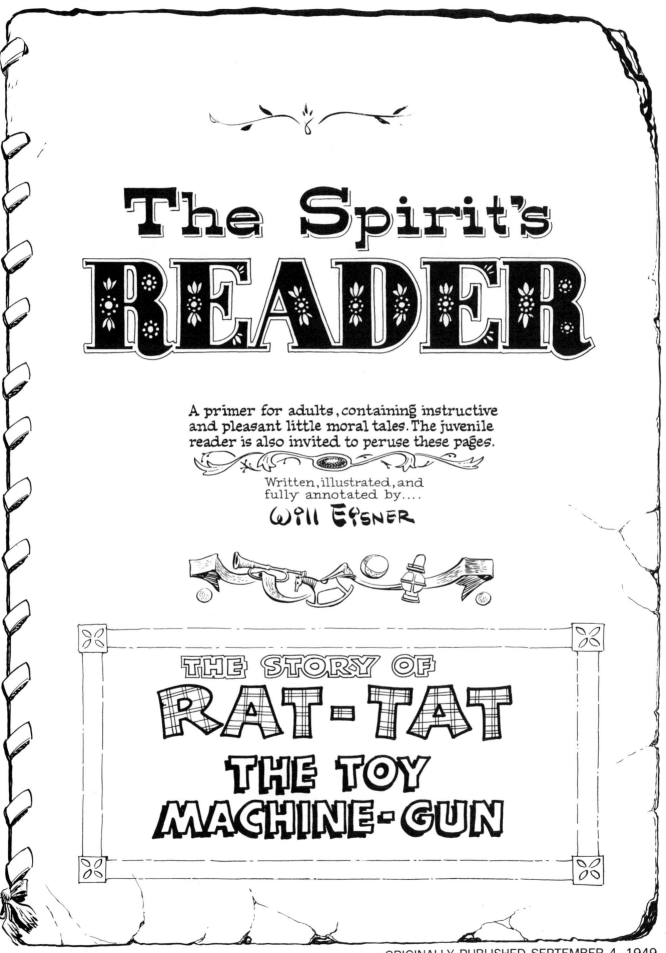

The Spirit's
READER

A primer for adults, containing instructive
and pleasant little moral tales. The juvenile
reader is also invited to peruse these pages.

Written, illustrated, and
fully annotated by....

Will Eisner

THE STORY OF
RAT-TAT
THE TOY
MACHINE-GUN

ORIGINALLY PUBLISHED SEPTEMBER 4, 1949

This is Rat-Tat.

Rat-Tat is a toy machine gun.

All day long Rat-Tat would go...

RAT A TAT
RAT A TAT

... and the little boys would go...

A-A-A-A-A-A
A-A-A-A-A-A

TOY DEPT.

UGH... Y'GOT ME!

And even though everybody pretended he was real, Rat-Tat knew.

Deep inside, he knew. He knew he was merely an imitation.

AN ACTOR, THAT'S ALL... A CHEAP HAM ACTOR...

And Rat-Tat's greatest dream was that some day he might become a real deadly weapon, like Max the Chopper.

TOY DEPT. SALE REDUCED

SPORTING ARMS DEPT. SALE

2

Then one day...

And in the confusion, Rat-Tat found himself a member of the awful Carbunkle mob.

A member, yes... but only a 'junior' member... for, let us face it, Rat-Tat was after all only a toy!

So Rat-Tat became a gang-gun... junior grade, of course.

Well, sir... the next night...

Oh dear, oh dear...

Through the rain and storm, through the smoke and flame ran Rat-Tat and the little kid.

SOB ...DEY'LL NEVER GIT US !!

Now Rat-Tat knew what it meant to be hunted. Adventure, danger... everything he had always longed for was now his.

WE'RE HOT! WE'LL SPLIT UP FER A WEEK AN' MEET AT DE HIDEAWAY!

But he was *scared!*

Hiding in alleys, cowering in sewers.. this was not at all the kind of life he had expected.

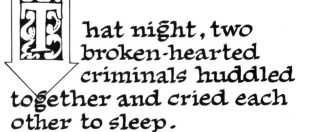

That night, two broken-hearted criminals huddled together and cried each other to sleep.

ow everything was spoiled... the bad Carbunkle boys were getting even worse.

HE'S ONLY WOUNDED!

YEAH, STUPID! LET'S DIVIDE THE LOOT, AND WE'LL FINISH THE SPIRIT OFF LATER!

Poor Rat-Tat was simply at his wits' end. He just didn't know what to do..

GOLLY... Y'GOTTA GET UP... THEY'RE GONNA KILL YA!

Wait... wait a moment... the Spirit was getting up.

BANG BANG

Oh dear... yes... he is up and fighting!

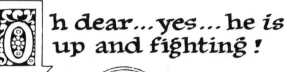

Poor Rat-Tat worried only harder.

If only there were something he could do... if only he were real!

GO 'WAY, KID... Y'BODDER ME AIM! I'M GONNA BLAST D'SPIRIT DIS TIME!

NO.. NO... Y'CAN'T SHOOT HIM... STOP..

130

ith every ounce of energy in his plastic body, Rat-Tat tried.

 hen the flames were out...

I OWE IT ALL TO THAT BOY'S QUICK THINKING. THE FLINT SPARKS FROM THAT BOY'S TOY GUN SET THEIR GASOLINE-SOAKED CLOTHES AFIRE AND GAVE ME TIME TO GET TO MY FEET!

BRAVE LAD.

POLICE Dept. CENTRAL CITY

nd tried...

nd **TRIED!**

ZZZzzzt

nd that day, Rat-Tat was as 'real' as any gun he had ever known...

nd much to everyone's surprise (including Rat-Tat's)

WHOOSH

...and sort of glad he was only a toy.

The END

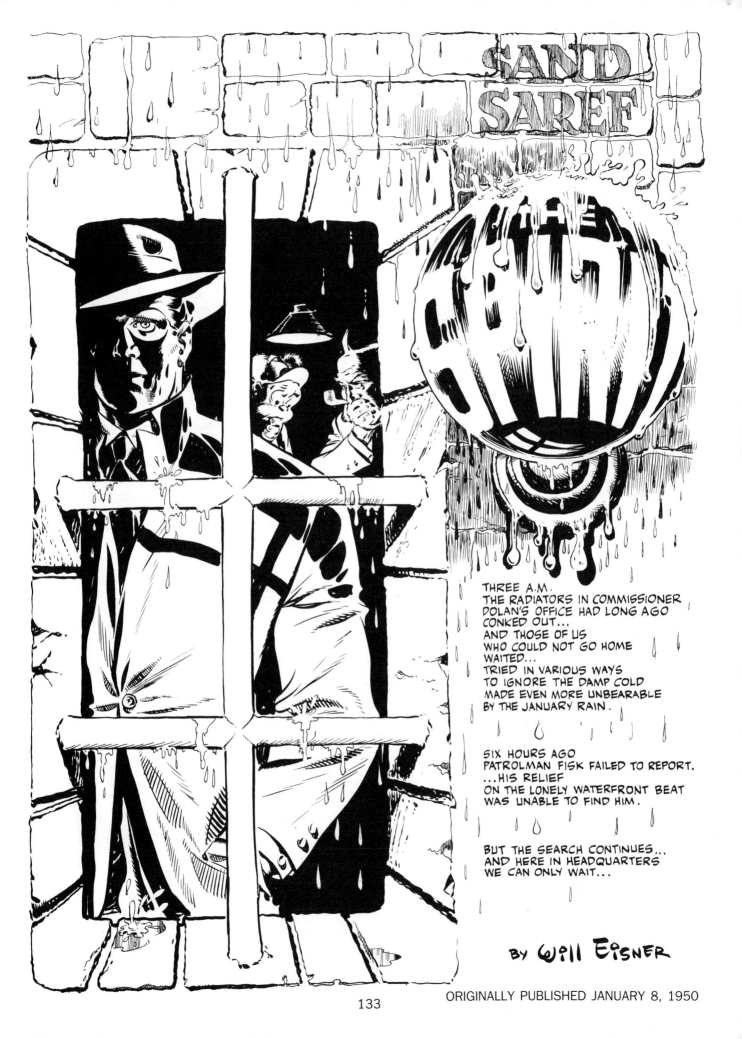

SAND SAREF

THREE A.M.
THE RADIATORS IN COMMISSIONER
DOLAN'S OFFICE HAD LONG AGO
CONKED OUT...
AND THOSE OF US
WHO COULD NOT GO HOME
WAITED...
TRIED IN VARIOUS WAYS
TO IGNORE THE DAMP COLD
MADE EVEN MORE UNBEARABLE
BY THE JANUARY RAIN.

SIX HOURS AGO
PATROLMAN FISK FAILED TO REPORT.
...HIS RELIEF
ON THE LONELY WATERFRONT BEAT
WAS UNABLE TO FIND HIM.

BUT THE SEARCH CONTINUES...
AND HERE IN HEADQUARTERS
WE CAN ONLY WAIT...

BY WILL EISNER

ORIGINALLY PUBLISHED JANUARY 8, 1950

THAT MAKES SIX GAMES IN A ROW! NOW, COMMISH, LET ME GIVE YOU SOME ADVICE...

LISSEN.. Y'LITTLE PIPSQUEAK I PLAYED CHECKERS LONG BEF...

RING RING RING RI

DOLAN SPEAKING.

YEP... UH HUH... RIGHT.. NO.. DON'T DO ANYTHING ELSE. I'M COMING RIGHT OVER.

DOLAN... WHAT..?

THEY'VE JUST FOUND FISK BADLY WOUNDED... MAYBE DEAD BY NOW!

I HAD MY ANSWER A FEW MINUTES LATER, IN THE FROSTBITTEN MUD-FLATS BARED BY THE OUT-BOUND TIDE.

SHOT IN THE CHEST. STILL BREATHING, BUT IN TERRIBLE SHAPE. GET HIM TO THE POLICE HOSPITAL.

SCOUR EVERY INCH OF THIS PLACE. IN A FEW HOURS, THE TIDE'LL BE BACK IN... AND THERE WON'T BE A CLUE LEFT...

IF THERE IS A CLUE...

HEY.. SPIRIT, I... HEY...

HE'S GONE!

I SAW HIM PICK UP A PIECE OF PAPER AND WALK OFF!

LET'S LOOK AROUND FOR HIM... HE MUSTA FOUND AN IMPORTANT CLUE...

BEST NOT, COMMISSIONER ...THESE MUD FLATS ARE TREACHEROUS, AND IT'S DARK. I'D WAIT TILL DAWN, SIR.

...I WALKED...WITHOUT PURPOSE...WITHOUT HEED...FOR IN MY POCKET WAS A PIECE OF CRUMPLED PAPER THAT, LIKE SOME MAGIC LODESTONE, SWEPT ASIDE THE VEIL OF MEMORY AND BROUGHT TO MY MIND THE DARKEST CORNERS OF MY LIFE. I WANTED TO BE ALONE...TO THINK BACK...TO REMEMBER...

I WALKED... LOST IN MEMORY... MY MIND SENT RACING BACK IN TIME BY A NAME SCRAWLED ON A CARD.."SAND SAREF"... WITHOUT THINKING, I FOUND MYSELF BACK IN DOLAN'S OFFICE AGAIN...

...ANY OTHER CASE... ANY OTHER CRIMINAL WOULD HAVE SENT ME OUT AFTER HIM LIKE A BLOODHOUND! BUT NOW I'VE GOT TO THINK.. IF IT WERE ONLY *ANYONE* BUT SHE!

WHO'S SAND SAREF?..WELL.. SAND SAREF WAS THE BIG LOVE IN MY YOUTH. ...IT'S HARD TO ERASE A THING LIKE THAT.

I FIRST MET SAND WHEN I WAS A KID IN THE SLUMS OF CENTRAL CITY'S LOWER EAST SIDE. I WAS LIVING WITH MY UNCLE AT THE TIME. HE WAS A HAS-BEEN FIGHTER. AS FOR SAND...HER FATHER WAS A COP...

OFFICER SAREF WAS A SQUARE, BRAVE COP... AND HE TOOK IT UPON HIMSELF TO LOOK AFTER MY POOR UNCLE, WHO WAS A PATSY FOR THE PETTY CROOKS THAT INFESTED OUR NEIGHBORHOOD. BUT ONE DAY....

SOMEONE'S COMING... LET'S GET OUT OF HERE!

HERE'S A ROD, Y'PUNCHY DOPE...LET 'EM HAVE IT..

MY UNCLE TRIED TO BACK OUT..HE WAS NO KILLER...

SHOOT, I SAID!

OH, F'CRYIN' OUT LOUD.. HERE, I'LL DO IT...

NO.. NO! IT'S OFFICER SAREF!

THE CROOKS FLED, LEAVING MY POOR BEWILDERED, GRIEF-STRICKEN UNCLE STANDING OVER THE CORPSE OF HIS GOOD FRIEND. HE DID THE ONLY THING HIS PUNCH-BATTERED BRAIN COULD TELL HIM. HE KILLED HIMSELF ON THE SPOT.

..WE TRIED TO CONTINUE AS PALS... BUT THE STRANGE TRAGEDY BEGAN TO HAVE ITS EFFECT ON US...

COPS..**COPS**..I HATE 'EM..**HATE 'EM**! IF MY FATHER WASN'T A COP, HE'D NEVER HAVE BEEN KILLED BY YOUR TWO-BIT CROOK OF AN UNCLE!

YEAH? TROUBLE IS, YOUR FATHER WASN'T A GOOD ENOUGH COP..IF HE WAS, HE'D UV SAVED MY UNCLE FROM...

SAND.. **SAND**..

I'M **SICK** OF YOU..I NEVER WANNA TALK TO YOU AGAIN!

ALONE NOW, SAND WAS CAUGHT IN THE UNDERTOW OF SLUM LIFE... AND SHE DIDN'T KNOW QUITE HOW TO HANDLE IT...

HMPF...THINKS SHE'S **SMART** JUST BECAUSE SHE'S GOT FOLKS AND I HAVEN'T.. I'LL SHOW 'EM **I CAN BE IMPORTANT** TOO!

HSSST... GIVE ME THOSE!

HEY... LITTLE GIRL... YOU **COME BACK** HERE...I SEEN YOU SWIPE THEM EARRINGS...

LEGGO!

WAIT, MISTER... **LET HER ALONE.** HERE'S YOUR EARRINGS...I..er.. **I TOOK 'EM!**

WHAT? YOU LITTLE THIEF!

HE STOLE A PAIR OF EARRINGS, OFFICER.

WHAT? DENNY COLT **STEALIN'**? I'M ASHAMED OF YE, DENNY. NOW GIVE 'EM BACK AND GO 'LONG WITH YE...IF YE DO IT AGAIN I'LL HAVE TO LOCK YE UP!

SAND... YOU DON'T HAVE TO **STEAL** TO GET THINGS Y'WANT. SHUCKS..I CAN GET Y'A **JOB** IN MR. GOLD'S GROCERY STORE AND YOU'D HAVE **ALL THE MONEY YOU NEED**.

IT'S NONE OF YOUR BUSINESS WHAT I DO.

AND DON'T THINK YOU HAVE TO TAKE CARE OF ME OR PROTECT ME.. **I HATE YOU... I HATE YOU!**

POOR KID... POOR KID.

BY 1942 AMERICA WAS WELL IN THE WAR... SAND HAD ACHIEVED AN INTERNATIONAL BACKGROUND... AS FOR ME... I WAS WITH AMERICAN INTELLIGENCE AND I COULD ONLY FOLLOW HER PROGRESS BY NEWSPAPER CLIPPINGS ...BELIEVE ME MISTER, THEY TOLD A LOT... THAT GIRL REALLY GOT AROUND!

Bring in Sand Saref....

ORIGINALLY PUBLISHED JANUARY 15, 1950

147

Satin

THE ISLAND OF PUERTO QUE IS ONE OF THOSE COUNTLESS PLEASURE-SPOTS THAT LITTER THE SEA SURROUNDING THE FAMOUS BARBADOS.

BARBADOS, YOU'LL REMEMBER, WAS A FAVORITE SPOT FOR BUCCANEERS OF OLD... TODAY, MODERN BUCCANEERS OF COMMERCE TAKE THEIR PLEASURE HERE IN COMFORTABLE MANSIONS.

THE SPIRIT
BY WILL EISNER

IT'S SAFE..IN FOREIGN TERRITORY... AND PRYING TOURISTS ARE KEPT AWAY BY THE HURRICANES!

NO...I WAS NOT THINKING OF A VACATION...NOR WAS THERE ANY CHANCE I'D SEE A HURRICANE..UNTIL THE DOOR TO DOLAN'S OFFICE SWUNG OPEN...

..AND SHE STEPPED IN..WINDBLOWN AND BEAUTIFUL..WITH AN AGELESSNESS THAT MADE ME THINK OF SORCERY...

SATIN !

ORIGINALLY PUBLISHED JUNE 12, 1949

AN INSTANT LATER..

SPIRIT.. DARLING.. IT'S BEEN SUCH A LONG TIME...

EASY, EASY...IT'S BEEN A LONG TIME, I'LL ADMIT...BUT BY THE RING ON YOUR LEFT HAND, YOU SHOULDN'T BE THROWING YOUR ARMS AROUND JUST **ANY** MAN!

I'M MARRIED NOW...TO KURT VAN BRECK..HE'S AN IMPORTER..WE MET IN SCOTLAND..LAST YEAR WE MOVED TO PUERTO QUE IN THE BARBADOS. YOU'D LIKE KURT. HE'S BEEN A WONDERFUL STEP-FATHER TO MY DAUGHTER HILDIE.

SATIN MARRIED.. SIGH... WHEN YOUR FIRST HUSBAND DIED, I THOUGHT... OH, WELL.. I HOPE YOU'RE HAPPY...

I WAS HAPPY, SPIRIT.. UNTIL A MONTH AGO, WHEN A MAN ON OUR ISLAND WAS BRUTALLY **MURDERED**!

HOW DOES THAT AFFECT YOU ?

NEXT WEEK, MY HUSBAND KURT WILL BE TRIED FOR THAT MURDER...AND I NEED **YOUR** HELP... TO PROVE HIM INNOCENT *!*

Y-YOU'LL COME, WON'T YOU? I MEAN, EVEN THOUGH HE'S MY HUSBAND..

YOU KNEW I WOULD, SATIN...

THE FLIGHT FROM CENTRAL CITY TO PUERTO QUE IS USUALLY PEACEFUL..BUT TODAY A HEAVY CONCENTRATION OF CLOUDS PILED UP ON THE HORIZON LIKE A GATHERING HORDE BEFORE AN ATTACK...I WAS TRYING TO PIECE THE STORY TOGETHER...

THE VICTIM'S NAME WAS SIR CLIVEDON PERCH. HE WAS A BRITISH DIPLOMAT... WHEN HIS BODY WAS WASHED ASHORE, KURT WAS ARRESTED !

...MOTIVE ?

THERE'S REALLY NO MOTIVE ! THE WHOLE AFFAIR IS RIDICULOUS !

DO YOU REALLY THINK KURT IS INNOCENT, SATIN ?

IT DOESN'T MATTER **WHAT** I THINK ! I HAVE A DAUGHTER ! HILDIE MUST NOT GROW UP BRANDED A MURDERER'S DAUGHTER ! KURT **MUST** BE PROVED INNOCENT !

FASTEN YOUR SAFETY BELTS ! WE'RE COMING IN TO PUERTO QUE !

AS THE PLANE LANDED DEEP IN THE INTERIOR, I COULD SEE THE LIGHTS ON ONE OF THE PLANTATIONS ILLUMINATING THE BLACK JUNGLE THAT COVERED PUERTO QUE.

MUSIC..?

A PARTY. KURT LOVES PARTIES.

UH-OH..A PLANE HAS JUST LANDED ! WE'D BETTER GO BACK TO THE HOUSE, KURT !

WHAT'S THIS?

THE SURF POUNDING THE SHORE HAD WASHED UP A TATTERED BRIEF CASE WITH A NAME ON IT...

SIR CLIVEDON PERCH!

THE WORLD TURNED BLACK AND GREEN...A HOLLOW ROAR FILLED MY HEAD AND I FELT AS IF I WERE IN THE MIDDLE OF A HURRICANE...
..I DIDN'T KNOW HOW RIGHT I WAS...

HILDIE!

SPIRIT... OH..ARE YOU ALL RIGHT? I WAS SO WORRIED... THOSE AWFUL MEN!

THEN IT WAS YOU I HEARD CRYING...YOU WERE DOWN HERE WATCHING ALL ALONG! THOSE WERE YOUR STEP-FATHER'S MEN, WEREN'T THEY? ANSWER ME, HILDIE!..FOR YOUR MOTHER'S SAKE...

I WON'T TELL YOU ANYTHING... I DON'T CARE WHAT HE'S DONE ..MOTHER LOVES HIM!

THANKS HILDIE...

I HEADED BACK UP THE WINDING ROAD... THE WIND WAS STRONG AND A GENTLE RAIN BEGAN TO FALL... BUT THIS WAS NOTHING TO THE STORM RAGING WITHIN ME...

KURT WANTED THAT BRIEF CASE PRETTY BADLY... PERHAPS BADLY ENOUGH TO KILL FOR IT!

AS I REACHED THE PORTICO, I HEARD LOUD SHOUTING...

SATIN...YOU FOOL...YOU BUMBLING FOOL... WHY DID YOU BRING HIM?

KURT.. PLEASE.. NOT SO LOUD..

I WAS CERTAIN TO BE ACQUITTED!! ... NOW THAT MASKED MEDDLER WILL RUIN EVERYTHING... GOOD NIGHT!

..BETTER LOOK IN ON KURT...

THE DISPATCH CASE..SO IT WAS KURT'S MEN WHO JUMPED ME...

WELL, WELL... TESTIMONY BY SIR CLIVEDON... HMM... SEEMS THAT KURT VAN BRECK WAS USING HIS IMPORTING FIRM TO SMUGGLE CONTRABAND FROM SOUTH ASIA!

...IF THESE PAPERS GOT AROUND, THEY MIGHT PROVE DAMAGING... MIGHTN'T THEY, KURT?

YES, SPIRIT...AND A MAN MIGHT EVEN MURDER TO GET THESE PAPERS! GIVE THEM BACK TO ME!

KURT, HAVE YOU SEEN HILDIE? I CAN'T FIND HER ANYWHERE! AND STORM WARNINGS ARE BEING POSTED ALL OVER THE ISLAND...A HURRICANE IS RISING!

THERE, LYING ON THE REEF, WAS HILDIE, HELPLESS BEFORE THE RAGING SEA...

LOOK, SPIRIT ...KURT IS DOWN THERE!

YES, BY GOLLY...HE'S TRYING TO SAVE HER!

I'LL GRAB HER!

SUDDENLY...THE CLIFF'S EDGE BEGAN TO CRUMBLE...

!

YEOW ??

CRRUNCH

..AND AN INSTANT LATER, KURT WAS SWALLOWED BY THE BOILING SEA..

YAAAH

SPIRIT!

STAY THERE, SATIN.. HILDIE IS ALL RIGHT...AND KURT...DIED... TO SAVE HER...

IT WAS A LONG TIME BEFORE EITHER OF US SPOKE...BUT AT LONG LAST THE HURRICANE PASSED INTO THE EAST... AND SATIN ASKED ME...

K-KURT.. WAS HE...

KURT DID A GREAT AND NOBLE THING...

NEXT DAY...PUERTO QUE AIRPORT...

SPIRIT...BEFORE YOU GO..PLEASE... I MUST KNOW... WAS HE GUILTY? DID YOU FIND ANY EVIDENCE?

I..I...HE'S DEAD NOW..IT DOESN'T MATTER ANY MORE... REMEMBER YOUR LATE HUSBAND AS A HERO...

I WATCHED SATIN AND HILDIE DISAPPEAR INTO TINY DOTS...AND THE ADVENTURE IN PUERTO QUE WAS BEHIND ME... KURT WAS DEAD...THE EVIDENCE AGAINST HIM COULD DO NO GOOD FOR ANYONE NOW...

SIR CLIVEDON PERCH

I LET THE SCRAPS OF PAPER FLY FROM THE WINDOW AND SCATTER IN THE WIND. THE SKY AHEAD WAS BRIGHT AND THE DAY WAS YOUNG...

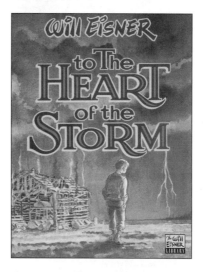

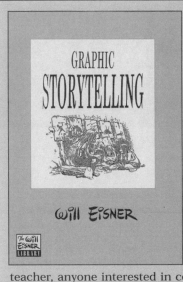

GRAPHIC STORYTELLING
New!

This companion volume to *Comics and Sequential Art* delves more deeply into the concepts and principles behind the creation of graphic narration. Designed for the young comics professional as well as the seasoned practitioner or teacher, anyone interested in comics as literature will find this a work of enduring value. Illustrated with scores of drawings by Eisner, as well as Al Capp, Milton Caniff, and many other masters of the medium.

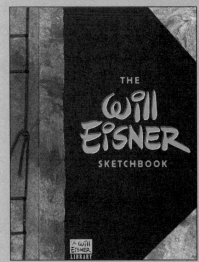

THE WILL EISNER SKETCHBOOK
New!

The father of the graphic novel provides his legions of fans with a behind-the-scenes look at the creation of his masterpieces in this, the first Eisner sketchbook ever published. Follow Eisner's creative process from character design to the final narrative. Included are the geneses of masterworks such as *Dropsie Avenue, The Building, To the Heart of the Storm,* and rare sketches from *The Spirit.*

COMICS AND SEQUENTIAL ART

Eisner covers all the bases in creating comic art in this "textbook" of sequential art. A distillation of Eisner's ideas, theories, and advice on graphic storytelling, the volume also includes a consideration of the many uses of the comic book art form. Profusely illustrated with his own work.

THE CHRISTMAS SPIRIT

Winner of the 1995 Eisner Award for Best Reprint!

Nearly every Christmas between 1940 and 1951, Will Eisner conjured up special Spirit stories. Now these nine poignant Spirit tales are available in one collection, in their original newspaper strip color. Included are "Darling's First Christmas," "S. Kringle Klaus," and seven other classics. With an introduction by Eisner. A perfect Christmas gift for the comics fan, young or old!

A LIFE FORCE

"A masterpiece! An uplifting book. It's given me encouragement to continue on in this medium."

–R. Crumb

Set during the Depression, *A Life Force* tells the hard luck story of a tenement dweller living in the same Bronx neighborhood that served as the setting for *A Contract With God*. Eisner's everyman, Jacob Shtarkah, and his family and neighbors come to life in this moving urban portrait.

SPIRIT CASEBOOK

The Spirit, which has influenced all subsequent comic book artists and writers, is a noiresque detective classic featuring comics' greatest femme fatales. Eighteen classic *Spirit* stories from the post-World War II era, including "Life Below," "Meet P'Gell," "Bring in Sand Saref," the sublime "Lorelei Rox," and "Gerhard Shnobble," the story of the man who could fly.

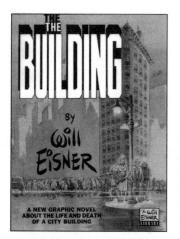

THE BUILDING

Four ghosts appear when a memory-filled building is demolished. *The Building* tells the stories of the ghosts, all connected in some way to the building–Monroe Mensh, whose life is suddenly altered by tragedy; Gilda Green, trapped in an unhappy marriage; P.J. Hammond, who becomes obsessed by the building; and street musician Antonio Tonatti.

CITY PEOPLE NOTEBOOK

Eisner describes this book as a series of "outtakes" for what became *New York: The Big City*. These quick stories, a few pages each, revolve around the environmental influences that all city dwellers feel: "Time," "Smell," and "Space." Eisner's panels capture the dark and the light, the bitter and the sweet of life in the modern metropolis.

THE DREAMER

A semi-autobiographical account of a young man who dreams of working in the budding comic book industry of the 1930's. Along the way he meets others who share his dream, and readers may recognize comics legends such as Bob (Batman) Kane and Jack (Captain America) Kirby. It is a work that captures the hopes and spirit of young artists in a new and untried medium–the comic book.

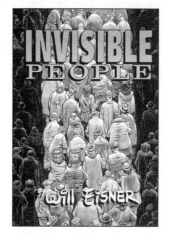

INVISIBLE PEOPLE

The extraordinary stories of four ordinary people you could pass on a city street any day. Linked by a common theme, this trio of portraits presents the dramatic turning points in three undistinguished lives, told with subtlety, irony and passion. Each story has a written preface by Eisner.

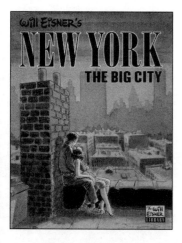

NEW YORK: THE BIG CITY

No other city in the world embodies man's loftiest aspirations and most base desires like America's greatest metropolis, New York City. In this perceptive graphic novel, Eisner examines the multi-faceted life of the city and its people, and all the flavor, color, and commotion that goes with it.

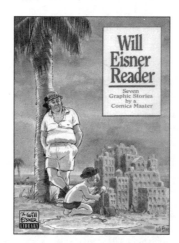

WILL EISNER READER

Collects seven of the best stories that originally appeared in *Will Eisner's Quarterly*–contemporary tales of poignant reality, imaginative forays into fantasy, ruminations on the human condition, and lighthearted exercises in whimsy. Included are "The Long Hit," "The Appeal," the lost classic "Sunset in Sunshine City," and four others.

THE SPIRIT COLLECTOR CARD SET

These thirty-six full color cards provide a complete guide to the characters and creators of the landmark *Spirit* series. In addition to the crime-busting Spirit are infamous villains such as the Octopus, femme fatales Sand Saref and P'Gell, Commissioner Dolan, Ellen, and Ebony White. Also included are creator cards with biographies of Eisner and his most famous assistant, Jules Feiffer.

 Write for a FREE Kitchen Sink Press catalog containing these Will Eisner works and hundreds of comic books, graphic novels, and related merchandise, or call **1-800-365-SINK (7465)**.